Bond

Assessment Papers

Fifth papers in Mathematics

J M Bond and Andrew Baines

Key words

Some special maths words are used in this book. You will find them **in bold** the first time they appear in the papers. These words are explained here.

acute angle — an angle that is less than a right angle

co-ordinates — the two numbers, one horizontal, the other vertical, that plot the position of an object on a grid, e.g. (4, 2)

edge — an edge is where two faces meet on a 3-D shape

factor — the factors of a number are numbers that divide into it,
e.g. 1, 2, 4 and 8 are all factors of 8.
e.g. 1, 2, 3, 4, 6 and 12 are all factors of 12.

HCF — abbreviation for highest common factor (see below)

highest common factor — The highest common factor of two numbers is found by first finding the common factors, then writing down the highest, e.g. the highest common factor of 8 and 12 is **4**.

icosahedron — a solid with 20 plane faces

integer — is a positive or negative whole number, e.g. $-6, 0, 3$

LCM — abbreviation for lowest common multiple (see below)

lowest common multiple — The lowest common multiple of two numbers is found by first finding the common multiples, then writing down the lowest, e.g. the multiples of 6 are 6, 12, 18, 24, 30, 36, 42, 48, 54, etc.
The multiples of 8 are 8, 16, 24, 32, 40, 48, 56, 64, 72, etc.
The common multiples of 6 and 8 are 24, 48, 72, etc.
So the lowest common multiple is **24**.

lowest term — the smallest you can make a fraction, e.g. $\frac{4}{10}$ reduced to the lowest term is $\frac{2}{5}$.

mean — a type of average. You find the mean by adding all the scores together and dividing by the number of scores, e.g. the mean of 1, 3 and 8 is 4.

median — a type of average. The middle number of a set of numbers after ordering, e.g. the median of 1, 3 and 8 is 3.
e.g. the median of 7, 4, 6 and 9 is 6.5 (half way between 6 and 7)

mixed number — a number that contains a whole number and a fraction, e.g. $5\frac{1}{2}$ is a mixed number.

mode — a type of average. The most common number in a set of numbers, e.g. the mode of 2, 3, 2, 7, 2 is 2.

obtuse angle — an angle that is more than 90° and not more than 180°

octahedron — a solid with 8 plane faces

parallelogram — a four-sided shape that has all its opposite sides equal and parallel

polygon — a 2-D shape with straight sides

prime numbers — any number that can only be divided by itself and 1, e.g. 2, 3 and 7 are prime numbers.

range — the difference between the largest and smallest of a set of numbers, e.g. the range of 1, 2, 5, 3, 6, 8 is 7 (8–1).

reflex angle — an angle that is bigger than 180° and less than 360°

rhombus — a parallelogram with four equal sides and diagonals crossing at 90°

trapezium — a four-sided shape that has only one pair of opposite parallel sides

vertex, vertices — the point where two or more edges or sides in a shape meet

Paper 1

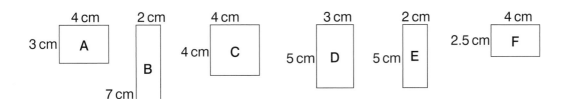

1 Area of A is _____ cm²

2 Area of B is _____ cm²

3 Area of C is _____ cm²

4 Perimeter of A is _____ cm

5 Perimeter of B is _____ cm

6 Perimeter of C is _____ cm

7 Area of D is _____ cm²

8 Area of E is _____ cm²

9 Area of F is _____ cm²

10 Perimeter of D is _____ cm

11 Perimeter of E is _____ cm

12 Perimeter of F is _____ cm

12

13 Which of the following numbers is divisible by 3, 4 and 10?

    40   30   60   50   90   _____

1

The ratio of girls to boys in a class of 25 children is 3:2.

14 There are _____ boys.   15 There are _____ girls.

2

Write the number which is:

16 2 less than 700 _____   17 10 more than one thousand _____

18 20 less than 2000 _____   19 30 more than 2890 _____

4

Class 4A has 25 children. One day 6 were absent.

20 What was the ratio of children who were present to children who were absent?   _____

21 What fraction of the class was present?   _____

22 What fraction was absent?   _____

23 What percentage of the class was away? _____ %

24 What percentage of the class was present? _____ %

25–28

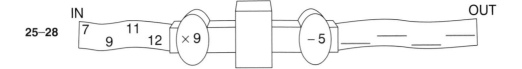

IN
7
9
11
12
$\times 9$
-5
OUT

29 $3 \times \triangle = 30 - 12$ $\triangle =$ _____

30 $\triangle \div 3 = 20 - 11$ $\triangle =$ _____

31 $3x = 25 + 2$ $x =$ _____

32 $2x + 1 = 36 \div 4$ $x =$ _____

The answers to the questions will be found in the sausage shape.

33 $13^2 =$ _____

34 $20^2 =$ _____

35 $2^2 + 2^2 =$ _____

36 $3^2 + 4^2 =$ _____

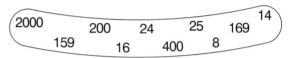

2000   200   24   25   169   14
159   16   400   8

37–40 Complete the shapes below. The dashed line is the line of symmetry.

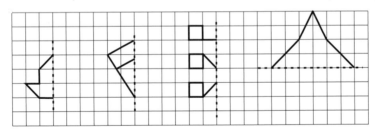

Fill each space with the sign > or < to indicate which is the larger.

41 1.7 kg _____ 1657 g

42 1.8 l _____ 1801 ml

43 days in July _____ days in June

44 $(3\frac{1}{2} + 2\frac{1}{4})$ _____ $(7\frac{1}{2} - 2\frac{1}{4})$

45 days in 2003 _____ days in 2004

46 (8×7) _____ (5×11)

47 20 hours _____ 1 day

48 4.9 cm _____ 56 mm

49   £
27.85
+36.97
_____

_____

50   £
41.10
−27.19
_____

_____

5

4

4

4

4

8

2

50
TOTAL

4

Paper 2

If a shape looks exactly the same when it is rotated about a point, it has rotational symmetry. The number of times it can be turned and still look the same is its order of rotational symmetry.

Examples

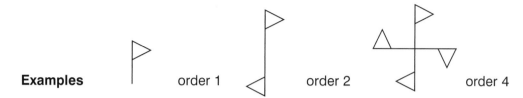

order 1   order 2   order 4

What is the order of rotational symmetry for the following shapes?

1 Rectangle   order _____

2   order _____

3 Regular pentagon   order _____   `3`

Look at this prism. How many faces, **vertices** and **edges** does it have?

4 Number of faces   _____

5 Number of vertices   _____

6 Number of edges   _____   `3`

Write the number of degrees contained in each of the following angles.

One right angle   Two right angles   Half a right angle

7 _____ °   8 _____ °   9 _____ °

$\frac{1}{6}$ of a circle   Three right angles $1\frac{1}{2}$ right angles

10 _____ °   11 _____ °   12 _____ °   `6`

5

13–14 Circle the two **prime numbers**.

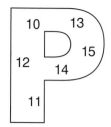

Find the cost of posting the following.

Airmail (Europe)	
Weight up to and including:	Cost
20 g	£0.37
60 g	£0.68
100 g	£0.99
160 g	£1.44
200 g	£1.74
260 g	£2.19
300 g	£2.49
360 g	£2.94

15 2 letters, each weighing 50 g

16 3 letters, each weighing 18 g

17 1 letter weighing 150 g and 1 weighing 270 g

18 1 letter weighing 320 g and 1 weighing 180 g

19 How much change would you get from £10.00 after posting 3 letters, each weighing 310 g?

20 How much change would you get from £20.00 after posting 5 letters, each weighing 280 g?

21–24 Complete this table.

3	12	4	_____	30	14
9	144	_____	121	_____	_____

25 $\frac{1}{2} + \frac{7}{8} =$ _____

26 $1 - \frac{7}{10} =$ _____

27 $\frac{3}{4} \times \frac{6}{9} =$ _____

28 $\frac{6}{9} \div \frac{2}{3} =$ _____

2

6

4

4

Round the numbers below to the nearest 10.

29 78 _____ **30** 91 _____ **31** 105 _____

32 63 _____ **33** 243 _____ **34** 367 _____

35 474 _____ **36** 1012 _____

8

37 7.8 + 12.95 + 0.176 = _____ **38** From 20.2 take 17.07 _____

39 Multiply 35.6 by 1.1 _____ **40** Divide 72.8 by 0.4 _____

4

A number is squared when it is multiplied by itself.

Example $10^2 = 10 \times 10$. From this we see that 10 is the square root of 100.

Write the square root of the following.

41 49 _____ **42** 121 _____ **43** 81 _____ **44** 144 _____

4

Card labels for presents are sold in packs costing 80p per pack. Use the graph to answer the following questions.

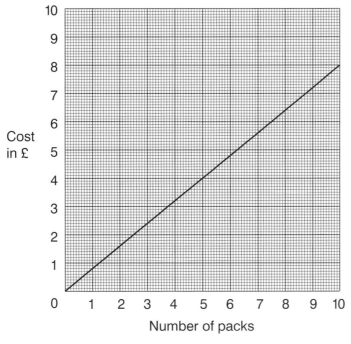

Cost in £ / Number of packs

45 How many packs can I buy with £7.20? _____

46 How much would 15 packs cost? _____

47 How much would 20 packs cost? _____

48 How many packs could I buy for £24.00? _____

49 How many packs could I buy for £20.00? _____

50 How much would 12 packs cost? _____

6

50
TOTAL

Here is a graph which shows the percentage of boys and girls who passed a certain test during a 5-year period.

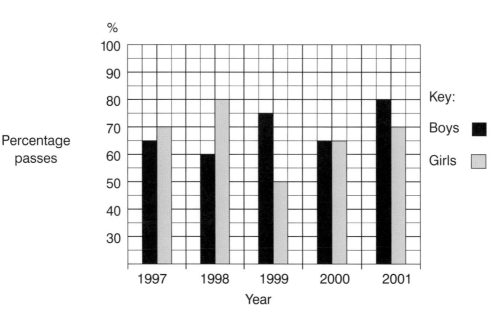

Number of packs

1   In which year did the boys achieve their highest pass rate? _____

2   In which year did the girls achieve their highest pass rate? _____

3   Which was the worst year for boys? _____

4   Which was the worst year for girls? _____

5   In 1998, 140 girls took the test. How many passed? _____

6   In 2000, 120 boys took the test. How many passed? _____

7   In which year was there no difference in the pass rate
    of the boys and girls? _____

8   The **mean** percentage of passes for the boys over this period was _____

9   The mean percentage of passes for the girls over this period was _____

    9

Look carefully at this number, then answer the questions.

     135.79

10   Which digit is in the hundreds place? _____

11   Which digit is in the units place? _____

12   Which digit is in the tenths place? _____

     3

Now look at this number.

46.253

13 Which digit is in the tens place? _____

14 Which digit is in the hundredths place? _____

15 Which digit is in the thousandths place? _____

If q = 4p + 2, complete the table below.

p	2	3	5	7
q = 4p + 2	_____	_____	_____	_____

16–19

Name these shapes. Choose names from the list below.

square   hexagon   **rhombus**   pentagon   **parallelogram**   octagon

20 _____   **21** _____   **22** _____

Here is a pie chart which shows what Jackie did with the £48.00 she was given for Christmas. Work out the following.

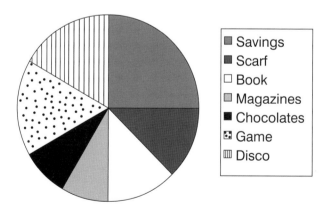

■ Savings
■ Scarf
□ Book
▨ Magazines
■ Chocolates
▣ Game
▥ Disco

23–24 She saved _____ . The scarf cost _____ .

25–26 The game cost _____ . The chocolates cost _____ .

27–28 The book cost _____ . The magazines cost _____ .

29 Jackie spent _____ at the disco.

Here is a pictogram which shows how many people went to the Cyber Café last week.
Use it to complete the table below.

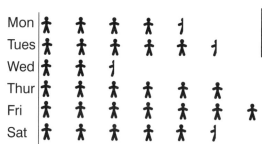

Mon
Tues
Wed
Thur
Fri
Sat

Key
= 50 people

30–35

The number of people who visited the café on:	
Monday was _____	Tuesday was _____
Wednesday was _____	Thursday was _____
Friday was _____	Saturday was _____

6

36 How many more people went to the café on Thursday than on Wednesday? _____

37 What is the **range** of the number of people who visited each day? _____

38 On which two days did the same number of people go to the café?

_____ and _____

39 What was the mean number of people who visited the café each weekday (not including Saturday)? _____

40 Which day do you think was early closing day? _____

5

Underline the correct answer.

41 $\frac{1}{2} - \frac{1}{8}$ = $\frac{1}{6}$ $\frac{1}{10}$ $\frac{3}{8}$ $\frac{1}{2}$ $\frac{1}{4}$

42 $\frac{3}{4} \times \frac{1}{4}$ =   1 $\frac{1}{4}$ $\frac{4}{8}$ $\frac{4}{16}$ $\frac{3}{16}$

43 10% of 50 =   5   45   10   40   15

44 The number of hours in 3 days =   60   36   84   72   90

45 The number of seconds in 5 minutes =   60   300   360   120   200

46 $\frac{1}{2} \div 4$ =   2 $\frac{1}{2}$ $\frac{1}{8}$ $\frac{3}{8}$ $\frac{3}{5}$

6

Work out the following.

47 700 ÷ 25 = _____   48 98.4 ÷ 24 = _____

49   364
    ×   25
    _____

    _____

50   173
    ×   3.6
    _____

    _____

4

50
TOTAL

Paper 4

Find the surface area of these cubes.

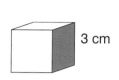 3 cm

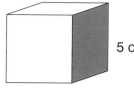 5 cm

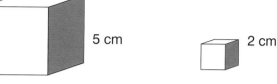 2 cm

1 _____ cm²

2 _____ cm²

3 _____ cm²

| | 3 |

Alison waited for the Christmas sales before buying new clothes. She went to her favourite store where the prices were cut by 20%. Complete this table.

4–13

	Usual price	Sale price	Saving
Skirt	£25.00	_____	_____
Sweater	£20.00	_____	_____
Shoes	_____	£16.00	_____
Jacket	_____	_____	£5.00
Jeans	£18.00	_____	_____

14 Altogether, Alison spent _____ on her new clothes.

15 She saved _____ by waiting for the sales.

| | 12 |

Fill in the missing **factors** of the following numbers.

16 The factors of 21 are   1   3   _____   21

17–19 The factors of 18 are   _____   2   _____   6   _____   18

| | 4 |

20 Share 48 items in the ratio of 3:5   _____ : _____

21 Share 27 items in the ratio of 7:2   _____ : _____

22 Share 36 items in the ratio of 5:4   _____ : _____

23 Share 66 items in the ratio of 8:3   _____ : _____

24 Share 108 items in the ratio of 9:3   _____ : _____

| | 5 |

Multiply each number below by 100.

25 47.6 _____   **26** 12 _____

27 7.2 _____   **28** 355.8 _____   **29** 0.014 _____

| | 5 |

In each of the classes below there are 30 children. The table shows attendances for one week this term. Write the mean attendance for each class.

	Class 1A	Class 1B	Class 2A	Class 2B
Monday	27	28	30	30
Tuesday	28	23	29	25
Wednesday	30	24	28	28
Thursday	25	25	28	26
Friday	25	25	30	21
30–33 Mean attendance	_____	_____	_____	_____

34 On which day were there the most children at school? _____

35 On which day were the fewest children present? _____

36 Which class had full attendance on two days? _____

37 Which class had the lowest attendance on any one day? _____

8

Write the following numbers in figures.

38 Twenty-three thousand and seventeen _____

39 Four hundred and two thousand and forty-two _____

40 Five hundred and fifteen thousand, five hundred and five _____

41 Ninety thousand, seven hundred and nine _____

42 One hundred and one thousand and seven _____

43 Fifty-seven thousand, five hundred and seventy _____

6

Find the cost of the following. £

44 4 kg of carrots @ 68p per kg _____

45 $2\frac{1}{2}$ kg of sprouts @ £1.30 per kg _____

46 $1\frac{1}{4}$ kg of onions @ 44p per 500 g _____

47 Total cost _____

48 How much change would you get from a £10 note? _____

5

Measure these lines to the nearest millimetre.

49 _____ _____ mm

50 _____ _____ mm

2

50
TOTAL

Paper 5

Name the following quadrilaterals.

Choose from square, rectangle, rhombus, parallelogram, **trapezium**.

1 _____

2 _____

3 _____

Simplify the following expressions.

4 a + a + a = _____

5 a + 2a + a = _____

Look at the shape below. Write the **co-ordinates** of each corner, starting at A and going in a clockwise direction.

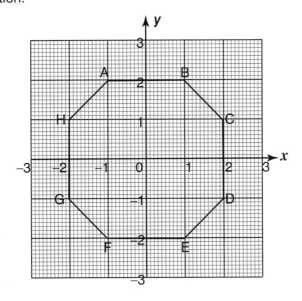

6 A (_____ , _____)

7 B (_____ , _____)

8 C (_____ , _____)

9 D (_____ , _____)

10 E (_____ , _____)

11 F (_____ , _____)

12 G (_____ , _____)

13 H (_____ , _____)

14 What is the name of this shape? _____

I have a normal pack of 52 playing cards.
Give your answers as fractions in their **lowest terms**.

15 What chance is there that I can draw out a red card? _____

16 What chance is there that I can draw out a spade? _____

17 What chance is there that I can draw out a king? _____

18 What is the chance that I can draw out a black ace? _____

19 What is the chance that I can draw out a red queen? _____   `5`

Find the **median** of:

20 5 15 20 10 30   The median is _____

21 19 12 24 18 17   The median is _____

22 36 8 27 22 24   The median is _____

23 10 80 70 60 50   The median is _____   `4`

24 The product of two numbers is 432. One number is 12, what is the other? _____

25 The sum of two numbers is 210. The larger is 179, so the smaller is _____   `2`

26–31 Here is the timetable of class 4a. Each lesson is 40 minutes long and the break lasts 20 minutes. Complete the timetable.

	Begins	Ends
First lesson	9.10	_____
Second lesson	_____	_____
Break	_____	10.50
Third lesson	10.50	_____
Fourth lesson	_____	12.10

`6`

A group of children were asked what they did last Saturday morning. Some helped with the shopping, some went for a swim, others went to the club, and 8 went to the library.

32 How many children were asked? _____

33 How many children went shopping? _____

34 How many went swimming? _____

35 How many went to the club? _____

36 What fraction of the children went to the library? _____

`5`

Put these containers in order of capacity by writing 1st in the space under the largest, and so on.

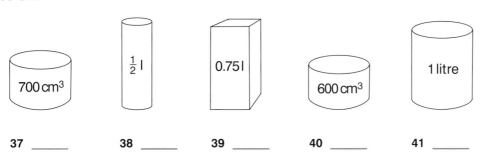

37 _____   38 _____   39 _____   40 _____   41 _____

Underline the correct answers in the following.

42 451 is divisible exactly by: 3   7   11

43 20 metres is: 2000 cm   200 cm   2000 mm

44 $3\frac{1}{3}$ is between: $3\frac{1}{2}$ and $3\frac{3}{4}$ 3.25 and 3.5   3.75 and 4.0

45 673 – 259 If I add 100 to each number the answer will be:

     200 more   the same   200 less

Our group, the 'Thumpers', made this flag.

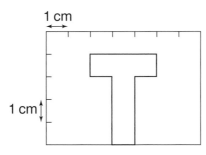

46 What is the area of the whole flag?   _____

47 What is the area of the 'T'?   _____

48 What is the area of the background?   _____

49 The perimeter of the flag is _____

50 The perimeter of the 'T' is _____

Simplify the following expressions.

1 3c + c + 2c = _____

2 5a – 3a + a = _____

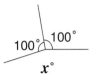

3 Angle x = _____ °

4 Angle y = _____ °

How many driving miles would you save if, instead of taking a ferry to St Malo, you sailed to Santander and then drove to your destination in Spain or Portugal? Complete the table below.

Destination	Port of arrival Santander	St Malo	Roscoff
Barcelona	450	719	747
Madrid	247	773	809
Alicante	508	940	976
Granada	518	1044	1080
Valencia	454	825	861
Marbella	628	1154	1190
Lisbon	553	1097	1133
Faro	626	1249	1209
Distance in miles			

5–8

Destination:	You would save (miles)
Lisbon	_____
Madrid	_____
Granada	_____
Marbella	_____

If you took the ferry to Roscoff instead of Santander, how much further would it be to drive to the following places?

9–13

Destination:	(miles)
Barcelona	_____
Alicante	_____
Valencia	_____
Madrid	_____
Lisbon	_____

5

Indicate which is larger by writing > or < in each space.

14 £3.54 _____ £3.45   15 €0.91 _____ €0.90   16 0.34 _____ 0.43

3

17
```
   4765
   8439
 +3856
 ------

 ------
```

18
```
  10000
 −  719
 ------

 ------
```

19
```
    478
 ×  304
 ------

 ------
```

20 1794 ÷ 78 = _____

4

Multiply each of the numbers below by 10.

21 1.06   22 21.004   23 3.5   24 0.708   25 0.035

____   ____   ____   ____   ____

5

26 It is Sunday 28th October and the clocks have been put back during the night as Summer Time has finished. Marianne has not altered her watch, which shows 8:30. What is the correct time? _____

1

27–30 Put these fractions in order of size, largest first.

$\frac{1}{12}$ $\frac{2}{3}$ $\frac{5}{6}$ $\frac{3}{4}$

____   ____   ____   ____

4

31 How many times can I fill a glass which holds 250 ml from a jug which holds 7.5 l? _____

32 What is the difference between 27 m and 413 cm? Give your answer in cm. _____

33–37 Complete this bar line chart which shows the heights of some children.

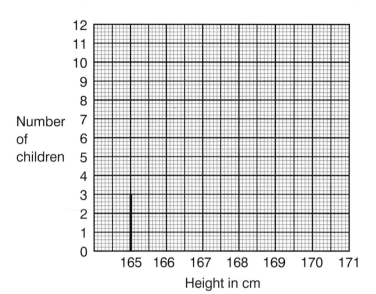

Number of children	Height (cm)
3	165
7	166
8	167
11	168
12	169
9	170

5

Write these times as you would see them on a 24-hour clock.

38 7:05 a.m. _____

39 12:30 a.m. _____

40 10:01 a.m. _____

41 11:04 p.m. _____

4

Give your answers to the following sums as **mixed numbers**, with fractions in their lowest terms.

42 $\frac{1}{2} + \frac{5}{8} =$ _____

43 $\frac{3}{4} + \frac{7}{16} =$ _____

44 $\frac{7}{8} + \frac{23}{24} =$ _____

45 $\frac{4}{5} + \frac{3}{10} =$ _____

4

46 Add together 78p, £7.99 and £3.75. _____

47 From 4 litres take 243 cm³. _____ cm³

2

48–50 Join up the equations which give the same value of p with a line.

3p + 5 = 12   3p = 10

3p – 4 = 13   3p = 7

3p + 2 = 12   3p = 17

3

50
TOTAL

1–3 Complete the table of values to satisfy the rule $y = x + 4$.

x	3	5	7	_____	20	24
$y = x + 4$	7	9	_____	13	_____	28

3

Fill in the missing number in each calculation.

4 $13.5 \times$ _____ $= 135$

5 $7.6 \div$ _____ $= 0.076$

6 $14.5 \div$ _____ $= 0.145$

7 $82.3 \times$ _____ $= 823$

8 $300 \div$ _____ $= 30$

9 $0.011 \times$ _____ $= 0.11$

10 $0.5678 \div$ _____ $= 0.005678$

11 $40.4 \times$ _____ $= 4040$

8

Match the percentages with the fractions. Write the correct letter in the space.

12 10% _____

13 25% _____

14 50% _____

15 75% _____

16 5% _____

17 20% _____

18 40% _____

19 60% _____

20 80% _____

(A) $\frac{1}{20}$

(B) $\frac{3}{5}$

(C) $\frac{3}{4}$

(D) $\frac{4}{5}$

(E) $\frac{1}{10}$

(F) $\frac{1}{2}$

(G) $\frac{2}{5}$

(H) $\frac{1}{4}$

(I) $\frac{1}{5}$

9

21–23 Underline the fractions below which are less than $\frac{1}{2}$.

$\frac{3}{7}$ $\frac{7}{10}$ $\frac{3}{4}$ $\frac{4}{9}$ $\frac{5}{6}$ $\frac{5}{11}$

3

If the last digit of a number is 5 or 0 then that number is divisible by 5.

Example 3245   the last digit is 5 so 3425 is divisible by 5

Underline the numbers that are divisible by 5.

24–26 3114   57530   4123   75505   341588   3415820

Underline the numbers that are divisible by 2.

27–29 3114   57531   4123   75505   341588   3415820

6

Remember to work out brackets first, then × and ÷ then + and –.
Find the answers to the following.

30 (4 + 5) ÷ (5 – 2) = _____

31 (22 – 18) × (9 + 2) = _____

32 (14 + 25) ÷ (15 – 2) = _____

33 (22 + 18) × (9 – 2) = _____

34 What is the temperature on the thermometer? _____ °C

Indicate which temperature is higher by writing > or < in each space.

35 –4 °C _____ 5 °C   **36** –3 °C _____ –2 °C   **37** –14 °C _____ –19 °C

Triangle A is rotated about the origin (0,0).

38–41 Which of the triangles B to H
are not a rotation of A about the origin?

_____   _____

_____   _____

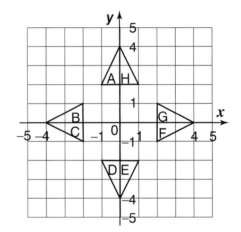

Using a protractor, measure the following angles to the nearest 10°.

42 _____   **43** _____   **44** _____   **45** _____

The letters from the word **ASSESSMENT** are placed in a tub, and a letter is taken out at random. Writing your answers as fractions in their lowest terms, what is the probability of taking out letter:

46 S _____   **47 E** _____   **48 M** _____   **49 T** _____

Simplify the following expression.

50 3c + 4d + 5d – c = _____

4

1

3

4

4

4

1

TOTAL

Paper 8

MERSEY FERRIES To Liverpool From Woodside			
	Mon–Fri	Sat	Sun
Hours	Minutes past the hour		
6	40	45	45
7	15 35 55	20 50	20 50
8	15 35 55	20 50	20 50
9	15 35 55	15 35 55	20 50
10	15 35 55	15 35 55	20 50
11	15 35 55	15 35 55	20 50
12	15 35 55	15 35 55	20 50
13	15 35 55	15 35 55	20 50
14	15 35 55	15 35 55	20 50
15	15 35 55	15 35 55	20 50
16	15 35 55	15 35 55	20 50
17	15 35 55	15 35 55	20 50
18	15 35 55	15 35 55	20 50
19	20 50	20 50	20 50
20	20 50	20 50	20 50
21	20	20	20

1 Write the time of the last boat each day in 12-hour-clock time. _____

2 How many boats are there between 6 and 7 a.m. Monday to Friday? _____

3 How many boats are there between 7 and 8 a.m. Monday to Friday? _____

4 How many boats are there between 7 and 8 a.m. on Sunday? _____

5 How many boats are there between 9 and 10 p.m. on Saturday? _____

6 The boats sail every _____ minutes between 7 a.m. and 7 p.m.
   Monday to Friday.

7 Between 7 a.m. and 7 p.m. on Sundays the boats sail every _____ minutes.

8 How many more boats are there on a Wednesday than on a Sunday? _____

Find the value for x which makes these equations true.

9 $x + 6 = 13$ $\qquad$ $x = $ _____

10 $x + 6 + 2 = 13$ $\qquad$ $x = $ _____

8

2

A parallelogram has all its opposite sides equal and parallel.
A rhombus is a parallelogram with four equal sides and diagonals crossing at 90°.
A trapezium has only one pair of opposite parallel sides.
A kite has two pairs of adjacent sides of equal length and no parallel sides. Its diagonals cross at 90°.

Name each of these shapes.

11  _____

12  _____

13 _____

14 _____

4

This pie chart shows which TV programmes are preferred by 72 children at a school. You are given the size of each angle.

15 How many children like music best? _____

16 The number who like sport best is _____

17 How many children like quiz programmes best? _____

18 The number of children who like horror films best is _____

19 How many children like soaps best? _____

20 How many children like drama best? _____

21 The number who like comedies best is _____

7

22–25 The shapes below are all regular. You are given the perimeter of each one. Work out the length of each side.

Perimeter	13.5 cm	11.0 cm	9.3 cm	14.0 cm
Length of one side	____	____	____	____

4

Write approximate answers to the following.

26 39×20 = _____

27 $39 + 69$ = _____

28 $300 \div 49$ = _____

29 $700 - 199$ = _____

30 $63 \times 101 =$ _____

31 $6000 \div 99 =$ _____

32 $48 \times 52 =$ _____

33 $179 + 19 =$ _____

`8`

34–40 Complete these fractions so that they are equivalent to 2.

$$2 = \frac{}{5} = \frac{}{11} = \frac{}{8} = \frac{}{7} = \frac{}{12} = \frac{}{27} = \frac{}{18}$$

`7`

Underline the correct number of:

41 degrees in the angles all round a point	300	90	180	360	540
42 hours in a week	140	168	24	60	186
43 metres in a kilometre	1000	100	10000	200	10
44 millimetres in 10 centimetres	10	1000	50	5	100
45 days in a leap year	365	360	165	366	200
46 pence in £100	1000	10000	100000	100	1100
47 minutes in $\frac{3}{4}$ hour	30	60	45	15	40
48 seconds in $\frac{1}{2}$ hour	30	18000	1800	6000	180

`8`

Measure the lines to the nearest millimetre.

49 _____ mm

50 _____ mm

`2`

`50`
TOTAL

Paper 9

Find the **mode**, median and range for the following values.

3   5   7   3

1 mode _____   **2** median _____   **3** range _____

5   8   4   8   3

4 mode _____   **5** median _____   **6** range _____

`6`

23

7 Reflect the flag F in the *y*-axis (vertical axis) and label it G.

8 Reflect the flag F in the *x*-axis (horizontal axis) and label it H.

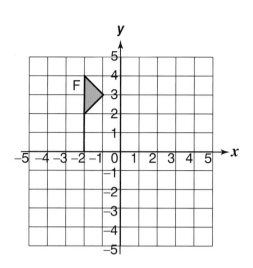

Find the value for *x* which makes these equations true.

9 $x + 6 + 2 = 13 + 2$ $x =$ _____

10 $x + 6 - 3 = 13 - 2$ $x =$ _____

Fill in the missing factors of the following numbers.

11–12 The factors of 35 are 1 _____ _____ 35

13–15 The factors of 24 are 1 2 3 _____ _____ _____ 12 24

16 $3\frac{3}{4} + 2\frac{7}{8} =$ _____

17 $7\frac{2}{3} + 4\frac{5}{9} =$ _____

18 $1\frac{3}{5} + 2\frac{3}{10} =$ _____

19 $8\frac{2}{7} + 3\frac{11}{14} =$ _____

20 $16.52 \div 7 =$ _____

21 $0.639 \div 9 =$ _____

22 $111.00 \div 4 =$ _____

23 $10.34 \div 11 =$ _____

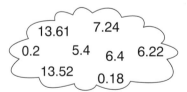

13.61 7.24
0.2 5.4 6.4 6.22
13.52 0.18

24–25 Which two numbers add to give 11.8? _____ _____

26–27 Which two numbers subtract to give 13.32? _____ _____

28–29 Which two numbers add to give 19.83? _____ _____

30–31 Which two numbers subtract to give 1? _____ _____

32–33 Which two numbers add to give 6.4? _____ _____

2

2

5

8

10

The area of a right-angled triangle $= \frac{1}{2} \times$ base length $\times$ height.

Find the areas of the following right-angled triangles.

34

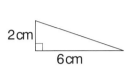

35

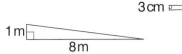

36

100 cm
3 cm

37

3 m

8 m

Area = _____ cm²   Area = _____ m²   Area = _____ cm²   Area = _____ m²

`4`

Write the numbers in the sentences in figures.

38 It was estimated that **eight and a half million** people watched the television programme.

_____

39 The population of Madrid is **two point nine million**.

_____

40 The footballer was transferred to Leeds United for **£12.2 million**.

_____

41 The building company made a profit of **£6.75 million**.

_____

`4`

Here is an approximate conversion table.
Use it to convert the measurements below.

Metric	Imperial
1 litre	$1\frac{3}{4}$ pints
1 kilogram	2.2 lb
8 kilometres	5 miles

42 4 litres ≈ _____ pints

43 10 kilograms ≈ _____ lb

44 40 kilometres ≈ _____ miles

45 _____ litres ≈ 14 pints

`4`

46–48 Complete the shapes below. The dashed line is the line of symmetry.

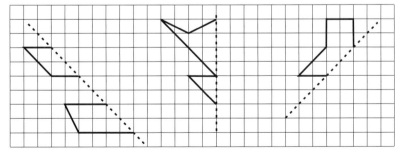

`3`

49 In a set of five tests Wasim got the following marks: 19   16   13   17   15.

What was his mean mark?

_____

`2`

50 After one more test his average mark was 15. How many marks did he score in the sixth test?

_____

`50`
TOTAL

Paper 10

1–3 Join up the equations which give the same value of m with a line.

$$5m + 3 = 8 + 7 \qquad\qquad 5m = 12$$

$$5m - 2 = 32 - 14 \qquad\qquad 5m = 19$$

$$5m + 6 = 4 + 21 \qquad\qquad 5m = 20$$

3

Complete this magic square containing the numbers 2 to 10. Remember that all the rows, columns and diagonals must add up to the same number (which is $\frac{1}{3}$ of the total number). The number in the middle square is $\frac{1}{9}$ of the sum of all the numbers.

4–10

7

Give the order of rotational symmetry of these shapes.

11 _____   **12** _____   **13** _____   **14** _____

4

15 $6^2 =$ _____   **16** $8^2 =$ _____   **17** $1^2 =$ _____   **18** $20^2 =$ _____

19 $9^2 =$ _____   **20** $11^2 =$ _____   **21** $14^2 =$ _____   **22** $50^2 =$ _____

8

The shapes below are made of cubes. Write the number of cubes in each shape.

23 _____   **24** _____   **25** _____

  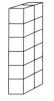

26 _____   **27** _____   **28** _____

6

29 $\frac{7}{8}$ of 40 = _____

30 $\frac{5}{9}$ of 27 = _____

31 $\frac{3}{7}$ of 28 = _____

32 $\frac{2}{11}$ of 66 = _____

4

Answer the following questions only using these words.

Certain   Likely   Unlikely   Impossible

33 I will eat some food today or tomorrow.   _____

34 I will eat a house today.   _____

35 It will not rain for two months.   _____

36 It will be sunny for the next twenty days.   _____

4

Here are some annual salaries. How much are they worth per month?

37 £25200   **38** £21840   **39** £13920   **40** £17880

_____   _____   _____   _____

4

A worker is paid £7.50 per hour. How many hours did he work to earn each of these amounts?

41 £150 _____   **42** £262.50 _____   **43** £67.50 _____

3

Here are 4 thermometers. What is the difference in temperature between each of the following?

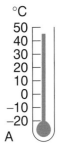
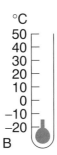
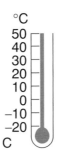
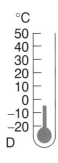

44 A and B _____ °C   **45** B and C _____ °C

46 C and D _____ °C   **47** A and D _____ °C

4

Look at this prism. How many faces, vertices and edges does it have?

48 Number of faces   _____

49 Number of vertices   _____

50 Number of edges   _____

3

50
TOTAL

Paper 11

SKI PACKS A child is anyone under 13 years old.		
Ski boots	Adult	Child
6 Days	€40	€30
13 Days	€77	€58
Ski school 2½ hours	Adult	Child
6 Days	€142	€100
Lift passes	Adult	Child
6 Days	€164	€124
13 Days	€286	€216
Skis & sticks	Adult	Child
6 Days	€78	€46
13 Days	€154	€90

Mr and Mrs Scott took their 11-year-old daughter to France for a 6-day skiing holiday. They hired the equipment and paid for it in Euros.

1 How much did it cost for all three of them to hire ski boots? € _____

2 How much did it cost for all three of them to hire skis and sticks? € _____

3 All three joined the ski school. How much did that cost? € _____

4 All three needed lift passes. How much was this? € _____

5 The total cost of all this was how much? € _____

6 At the time of their holiday €1.6 were equal to £1.

How much in pounds sterling did it cost to hire boots, skis and sticks for the family? £_____

7 In pounds sterling, the ski school cost £_____

8 In pounds sterling, the passes for the lift cost £_____

8

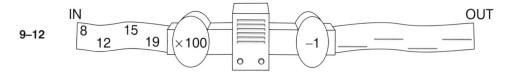

9–12 IN 8 12 15 19 ×100 −1 OUT

4

Change these fractions into percentages.

13 $\frac{16}{64}$ = _____   14 $\frac{15}{75}$ = _____

2

15–24 Draw lines of symmetry in the shapes below. Be careful, some shapes may have more than one line and others may have none.

10

Find the mean of these numbers.

25 7 $2\frac{1}{2}$ $1\frac{1}{2}$ 1   The mean is _____

26 4   7 $3\frac{1}{2}$ $5\frac{1}{2}$ The mean is _____

27 $2\frac{1}{2}$ $3\frac{1}{2}$ $4\frac{1}{2}$ $5\frac{1}{2}$ The mean is _____

Find the median of these numbers.

28 6   9   5   7   8   The median is _____

29 4   10   12   11   7   The median is _____

30 12   6   19   13   8   The median is _____

6

A class thought it would take exactly two minutes to run to the end of the field. Here are the times Mr Jones recorded.

31–36 Who was the nearest to two minutes? Put them in order in the table below.

Oliver	118 seconds
Kachanda	$2\frac{1}{4}$ minutes
Mali	107 seconds
Hermione	1 minutes 59 seconds
Chloe	2 minutes 12 seconds
Jay	2 minutes 3 seconds

	Name
The nearest was	_____
Then	_____
Then	_____
Then	_____
Then	_____
Furthest away was	_____

6

37–40 Underline the numbers which are exactly divisible by 10.

1365   1270   1111   1765   2100

8080   1235   1801   3000   1681

4

Using a protractor, measure the following angles to the nearest 5°.

41 _____   42 _____   43 _____   44 _____

4

45–48 What are the prime numbers less than 10?   _____ _____ _____ _____

4

Here are two irregular **polygons**. Say whether they are concave or convex.

49 _____   50 _____

2

50
TOTAL

Paper 12

	OCT	NOV	DEC	JAN	FEB	MAR	APR
Costa de Almeria							
Average daily hours of sunshine	7	6	6	6	6	7	8
Average daily max temp °C	20	15	10	8	9	12	15
London							
Average daily max temp °C	11	7	5	4	4	7	10

Use the table above to answer these questions.

1 In Costa de Almeria, which month has
   the highest average daily hours of sunshine?   _____

2 Which month has the highest average daily maximum
   temperature in Costa de Almeria?   _____

3 Which month has the highest average daily maximum
   temperature in London?   _____

4 What is the difference in average daily maximum temperature
   between London and Costa de Almeria in December?   _____ °C

5 Write the range of average daily maximum temperatures
   shown for Costa de Almeria.   _____ °C

6 How much difference is there between the highest and lowest
   average daily maximum temperatures shown for London?   _____ °C

7 In which month is there the least difference in average daily maximum temperatures between the two places? _____

8 What is the difference in temperature in that month? _____ °C

What is the sale price of each of these items, and what is your saving on each purchase?

**15%
off**

£150

9 Sale price £ _____

10 Saving £ _____

**10%
off**

£850

11 Sale price £ _____

12 Saving £ _____

**7½%
off**

£6

13 Sale price £ _____

14 Saving £ _____

**20%
off**

15 What is the original price of the camera if you save £22? £ _____

16 The temperature increases by 6 °C from 0 °C. What is the new temperature? _____ °C

17 The temperature decreases by 6 °C from 0 °C. What is the new temperature? _____ °C

18 The temperature increases by 3 °C from –4 °C. What is the new temperature? _____ °C

19 The temperature decreases by 6 °C from –2 °C. What is the new temperature? _____ °C

Below are some nets of solids and a list that will help you name them.

hexagonal prism   cube   **octahedron**   **icosahedron**

20

21

22

23

_____   _____   _____   _____

Here are the hand-spans in cm for Class 6B.

17	18	14	13	14	18	19
17	21	23	16	11	13	10

24–28 Complete this frequency table.

Hand-span (cm)	0–5	6–10	11–15	16–20	21–25
No of pupils	_____	_____	_____	_____	_____

29–32 Now complete the pictogram below for these values (including the key). The last row has been done for you.

Key
____ children = ☺

0–5 cm	
6–10 cm	
11–15 cm	
16–20 cm	
21–25 cm	☺

Here are the petrol gauges in 3 cars.

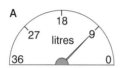 A 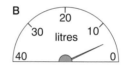 B 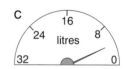 C

Petrol costs 69p per litre. In order to fill up their tanks:

33–34 A would need _____ litres.   This would cost _____

35–36 B would need _____ litres.   This would cost _____

37–38 C would need _____ litres.   This would cost _____

39 How much would it cost to fill all 3 cars?   _____

Give the size of the marked angles below.

40 _____ °   **41** _____ °   **42** _____ °   **43** _____ °

There are 660 pupils in a school; 55% of them are girls.

44 How many girls are in the school?   _____

45 How many boys are there?   _____

46–47 When you multiply 1243 by 4318 the last digit will end in a **4**, since 3×8 is **24**. Now use this information to circle the correct answer to each of the following questions.

$344 \times 328 =$ 112835   112832   112831   112839   112838

$2347 \times 46326 =$ 108727124   108727121   108727126   108727122   108727129

| 2 |

Write the following figures rounded correctly to one decimal place.

48 11.76 _____   **49** 10.91 _____   **50** 7.35 _____

| 3 |

| **50** |
| TOTAL |

Paper 13

Look at this prism. How many faces, vertices and edges does it have?

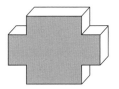

1 Number of faces _____

2 Number of vertices _____

3 Number of edges _____

| 3 |

P is a translation of A by **p**.

Translate the following shape A. Draw and label its new location each time.

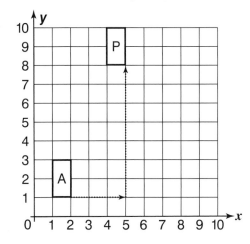

$\mathbf{p} = \begin{pmatrix} 3 \\ 7 \end{pmatrix}$

$\mathbf{b} = \begin{pmatrix} 4 \\ 0 \end{pmatrix}$ $\mathbf{c} = \begin{pmatrix} 0 \\ 3 \end{pmatrix}$ $\mathbf{d} = \begin{pmatrix} 2 \\ 1 \end{pmatrix}$ $\mathbf{e} = \begin{pmatrix} 5 \\ 6 \end{pmatrix}$ $\mathbf{f} = \begin{pmatrix} -1 \\ 4 \end{pmatrix}$

4 Translate A by **b** to B.   **5** Translate A by **c** to C.   **6** Translate A by **d** to D.

7 Translate A by **e** to E.   **8** Translate A by **f** to F.

| 5 |

Here is a table showing some approximate distances in km between different airports in the world.

	London	Paris	Moscow	New York	Hong Kong	Montreal
London		340	2500	5900	9500	5200
Paris	340		2480	6150	9600	5500
Moscow	2500	2480		7800	7100	7040
New York	5900	6150	7800		13000	780
Hong Kong	9500	9600	7100	13000		12400
Montreal	5200	5500	7040	780	12400	

9 London to Montreal is _____ km **10** New York to Montreal is _____ km

11 Moscow to Paris is _____ km **12** Hong Kong to London is _____ km

Give the total distance of a flight from:

13 New York to Moscow via London _____ km

14 Hong Kong to New York via Montreal _____ km

15 Paris to Montreal via Moscow _____ km

16 London to New York and back again _____ km `8`

Find the surface area of these cuboids.

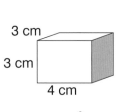

17 _____ cm²

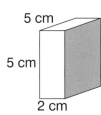

18 _____ cm²

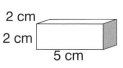

19 _____ cm² `3`

Estimate the answers to the following sums.

20 598 + 204 = _____

21 1212 − 297 = _____

22 39 × 31 = _____

23 902 ÷ 29 = _____

24 12124 ÷ 104 = _____

25 42 × 19 = _____ `6`

26 Subtract the smallest number below from the largest.

10.007   10.077   10.708   10.070   10.780   _____ `1`

27 The mean of four numbers is $5\frac{1}{2}$. If one of the numbers is 7, what is the mean of the other 3 numbers? _____

Three numbers multiplied together equal 2880.

$A \times B \times C = 2880$ $A \times B = 360$ $A \times C = 160$

28 A = _____   **29** B = _____   **30** C = _____

The flag is rotated three times about different points and different amounts of a full turn.

Each rotation starts about the position shown.

Draw each new position:

31 Half turn about (−1,0).

32 Quarter turn clockwise about (0,3).

33 Quarter turn anticlockwise about (−2,0).

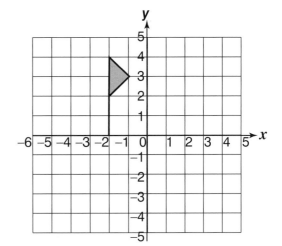

34–39 Put these in order, starting with the one which is the best value.

A 20 g for £2   B 25 g for £3   C 30 g for £4.20

D 10 g for £1.30   E 24 g for £2.64   F 40 g for £3.60

_____   _____   _____   _____   _____   _____

In a pack of 52 cards, what is the ratio of:

40 hearts to the other suits?   _____ : _____

41 aces to the other cards?   _____ : _____

I will roll a fair 6-sided dice. Writing your answers as fractions in their lowest terms, what is the probability of rolling:

42 a 4?   _____

43 an even number?   _____

44 a 7?   _____

45 a number less than 5? _____

46 a number less than 10? _____

'I think of a number then add five' is written as **n + 5**

Draw lines to join up the statements which are equal.

47 I think of a number then add two $\frac{n}{2}$

48 I think of a number then subtract three $n + 2$

49 I think of a number then multiply it by four $n - 3$

50 I think of a number then halve it $4n$

| 4 |

| **50** |
TOTAL

Paper 14

1 Find the width of a rectangle which is 7.5 m long, and has an area of 60 m².

2 If the area of a square is 225 cm² what is the length of one side?

| 2 |

3–6

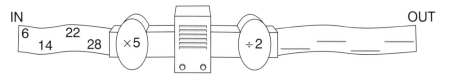

| 4 |

Underline the correct answer.

7 $3^2 =$ 9   27   6   33

8 1.5 m =   150 mm   15 cm   1500 cm   150 cm

| 2 |

9 What is the length of one side of an equilateral triangle if the perimeter of the triangle is 10.5 cm?

| 1 |

Give your answers to the following as mixed numbers, with fractions in their lowest terms.

10 $7\frac{1}{3} - 3\frac{4}{9} =$ _____

11 $3\frac{3}{10} - 1\frac{3}{5} =$ _____

12 $5\frac{2}{8} - 3\frac{11}{16} =$ _____

13 $4\frac{5}{6} - 2\frac{1}{18} =$ _____

| 4 |

Remember to work out brackets first, then × and ÷, then + and −.

Find the answers to the following.

14 $5 + 3 \times 2 =$ _____

15 $(12 - 2) \div 5 =$ _____

16 $54 - 4 \times 12 =$ _____

17 $65 + 25 \div 5 =$ _____

| 4 |

18 What is the temperature on the thermometer? _____ °C

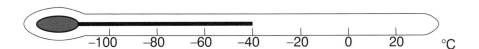

Indicate which temperature is higher by writing > or < in each space.

19 −43 °C _____ 52 °C

20 −31 °C _____ −23 °C

21 −140 °C _____ −191 °C

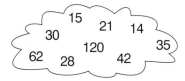

22–25 Write the multiples of 5 from the numbers in the bubble.

_____   _____   _____   _____

26–30 Write the multiples of 7 from the numbers in the bubble.

_____   _____   _____   _____   _____

31–35 'Multiply by seven then subtract three' can be written as **7n − 3**

Draw lines to join up the statements which are equal.

Multiply by three then add two	$\frac{n}{3} - 2$
Multiply by two then add three	$3n + 2$
Divide by two then subtract three	$3(n + 2)$
Divide by three then subtract two	$2n + 3$
Add two then multiply by three	$\frac{n}{2} - 3$

The letters from the word **MATHEMATICS** are placed in a tub, and a letter is taken out at random.

Writing your answers as fractions in their lowest terms, what is the probability of taking out letter:

36 S _____

37 E _____

38 M _____

39 T _____

1

3

9

5

4

Write either **acute**, **obtuse** or **reflex** to describe the angles on the shape below.

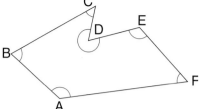

40 ∠ ABC _____

41 ∠ BCD _____

42 ∠ CDE _____

43 ∠ DEF _____

44 ∠ EFA _____

5

Angus, Belinda and Christine had £1.68 between them. After Angus paid back the 3p that he had borrowed from Belinda, and Christine had repaid 5p she had borrowed from Belinda, they found that Angus had twice as much as Belinda, and Belinda had twice as much as Christine.

45–50

At first:	Angus had _____	Belinda had _____	Christine had _____
Afterwards:	Angus had _____	Belinda had _____	Christine had _____

6

50
TOTAL

Paper 15

1–2 Write the next two terms in the following sequence.

13   17   21   25   _____   _____

2

Answer the following questions using only these words.

    Certain   Likely   Unlikely   Impossible

3 Next year there will be 55 Tuesdays. _____

4 The sun will set in the west tomorrow. _____

5 I will take a breath in the next twenty minutes. _____

6 In a year's time I will be one year older. _____

4

All these rectangles have the same perimeter. Find the missing lengths and the areas.

7–13

Perimeter	Length	Width	Area
24 cm	5 cm	7 cm	35 cm²
24 cm	_____	3 cm	27 cm²
24 cm	1 cm	_____	_____
24 cm	_____	10 cm	_____
24 cm	_____	_____	36 cm²

7

CHICAGO Illinois										Distances in miles
1020	**DENVER** Colorado									
270	1280	**DETROIT** Michigan								
1650	710	1900	**GRAND CANYON** Ariz.							
1090	1030	1340	1210	**HOUSTON** Texas						
1010	1700	1000	1800	920	**JACKSONVILLE** Flor.					
1770	780	2030	310	1420	2100	**LAS VEGAS** Nevada				
2100	1130	2350	530	1550	2390	280	**LOS ANGELES** Cal.			
1410	2060	1440	2310	1230	360	2520	2730	**MIAMI** Florida		
850	1860	570	2510	1860	1400	2590	2920	1790	**MONTREAL** Quebec	
940	1280	1090	1540	360	590	1720	1900	910	1640	**NEW ORLEANS** Louis.

Use the chart to answer these questions.

14 What is the distance between Chicago and Miami? _____

15 How far is it from Detroit to Houston? _____

16 The distance between Denver and Montreal is _____

17 The distance between Grand Canyon and New Orleans is _____

18 How much further is it from Jacksonville to Miami
than from Grand Canyon to Las Vegas? _____

19 Which two places listed are the
shortest distance apart? _____ and _____

20 Which two places listed are the
greatest distance apart? _____ and _____

21 Which two places are exactly
1700 miles apart? _____ and _____

22 Which two places are exactly
1000 miles apart? _____ and _____

9

39

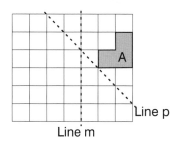

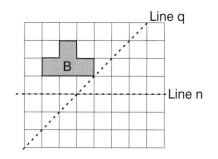

23 Reflect shape A in mirror line p.   Label it P.

24 Reflect shape A in mirror line m.   Label it M.

25 Reflect shape B in mirror line q.   Label it Q.

26 Reflect shape B in mirror line n.   Label it N.

4

27 A typist averages 14 words to a line and 30 lines to a page.
How many pages will be needed for 38406 words? _____

1

Car park charges	
Up to 1 hour	£1.00
1 to 2 hours	£1.20
2 to 3 hours	£1.40
3 to 4 hours	£1.60
4 to 5 hours	£1.80
5 to 6 hours	£2.00
6 to 7 hours	£2.20
7 to 8 hours	£2.40
Over 8 and up to 12 hours	£3.00

What would the following people pay?

28 Mr Singh parked from 11:30 a.m. to 1:15 p.m.   _____

29 Mrs Gee parked from 10:20 a.m. to 1:25 p.m.   _____

30 Mr Exe parked from 9:25 a.m. to 2:10 p.m.   _____

31 Mrs Ward parked from 8:30 a.m. to 5:05 p.m.   _____

32 Mr Wu parked from 1:05 p.m. to 2:10 p.m.   _____

33 Mrs Bell parked from 2:17 p.m. to 10:01 p.m.   _____

34 Mr Green parked from 10:44 a.m. to 4:05 p.m.   _____

7

Change these measurements to centimetres.

35   47.5 m _____   36   0.176 m _____

37   6.07 m _____   38   103.03 m _____

Change these measurements to metres.

39   0.37 km _____   40   11 km _____

41   0.002 km _____   42   4.15 km _____

8

Complete the table below.

Fraction	Decimal	Percentage
$\frac{9}{10}$	_____	_____ %
_____	0.01	_____ %
_____	_____	17%

43–48

6

Find the value for x in each of these equations.

49   $2x + 6 = 14$ $x = $ _____

50   $4x - 3 = 13$ $x = $ _____

2

50
TOTAL

Paper 16

1–2   Write the next two terms in the following sequence.

23   17   11   5   _____   _____

2

Here are some irregular polygons. Say whether they are concave or convex and name them. **Example** convex decagon

3–4   _____ _____

5–6   _____ _____

4

Here is part of a train timetable.

Train	Greasby	Upton	Moreton	Leasowe
A	13:15	13:23	13:29	13:50
B	14:09	→	→	14:38
C	14:23	14:32	14:39	14:59
D	15:01	→	→	15:31
E	15:58	16:07	16:14	16:32

7 Travelling from Greasby to Leasowe, which train is the fastest? _____

8 Which is the slowest? _____

9–10 Which trains are non-stop? _____ _____

11 If I cannot leave Greasby before 3:30 p.m.,
which of these trains must I catch? _____

12 How long does train E take to go from Greasby to Upton? _____

13 How long does train A take to travel from Upton to Leasowe? _____

I roll a fair 6-sided dice. Writing your answers as fractions in their lowest terms, what is the probability of rolling:

14 6? _____   15 an odd number? _____

16 a zero? _____   17 a number greater than 1? _____

18 a number less than 7 and more than 0? _____

Indicate which is larger by writing > or < in each space.

19 0.30 _____ 0.50   20 2.6 _____ 2.5

21 5.6 km _____ 5500 m   22 0.463 _____ 0.473

23–28 Some children from our school went on a day trip to London. The cost was £20.00 per child. Complete the table for the cost per class.

Class	Number in class	Number going on trip	Cost for the class
2a	30	6	_____
2b	30	7	_____
3a	30	8	_____
3b	30	4	_____
4a	30	13	_____
4b	30	12	_____

29–34 Now make a bar line chart to show how much money was collected from each class. Two numbers have been inserted to help you arrange the money in the best way.

35 What fraction of all the children from these classes went on this trip? _____

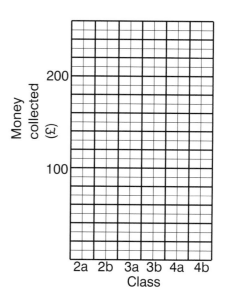

200

Money collected (£)

100

2a 2b 3a 3b 4a 4b
Class

7

Simplify the following expressions.

36 $6a + a + 3 =$ _____

37 $b + 4b + 4 =$ _____

38 $3c + 4 + 2 =$ _____

39 $5a - 2a + 5 =$ _____

4

Find the mode of the following series.

40	43	44	46	47	43	45	The mode is _____
41	101	110	111	100	10	110	The mode is _____
42	36	37	33	35	33	39	The mode is _____
43	21	31	22	21	32	23	The mode is _____

4

The perimeter of a piece of card is 100 cm and it is four times as long as it is wide.

44 The length is _____

45 The width is _____

What is the length of the side of a square with an area of:

46 196 cm² _____

47 289 cm² _____

4

What is the order of rotational symmetry of the following shapes?

Square

Regular hexagon

3

48 _____

49 _____

50 _____

50
TOTAL

Paper 17

1–3 Circle the three prime numbers.

16 17 18 19 20 21 22 23

3

Some pupils from Class 5 were asked how long it took them to get to school today. Here are their times in minutes.

| 34 | 42 | 46 | 41 | 32 | 38 | 37 | 24 | 23 | 28 | 27 |
| 32 | 41 | 44 | 43 | 33 | 38 | 36 | 22 | 21 | 26 | 27 |

4–9 Complete this frequency Table A.

Time (mins)	21–25	26–30	31–35	36–40	41–45	46 and over
No of pupils						

6

10–12 Now complete this frequency Table B.

Time (mins)	0–20	21–60	61–80
No of pupils			

3

13 Which frequency table do you think gives the most useful information about the time it took the pupils to get to school? _____

1

14 Area of whole shape _____

15 Area of shaded part _____

16 Area of unshaded part _____

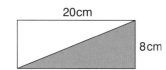
20cm

8cm

3

Triangle E is rotated about the origin (0,0).

17–19 Which of the triangles A to H are a rotation of E about the origin?

____ ____ ____

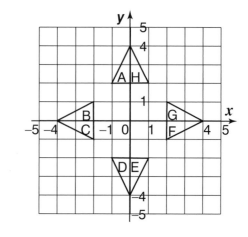

3

44

Underline the correct answer.

20 days in 2010 =   330   366   160   350   365

21 1% of 1000   =   100   10   1   1000   101

22 3030 m   =   303 km   30.3 km   3.03 km   3.003 km   0.303 km

23 515 cm   =   5.15 m   0.515 m   51.5 m   5150 m   515.5 m

24 40% of 25   =   65   15   12.5   8   10

> 5

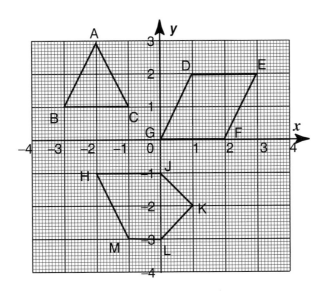

Give the co-ordinates of the letters:

25 A _____   **26** B _____   **27** C _____

28 D _____   **29** E _____   **30** F _____

31 G _____   **32** H _____   **33** J _____

34 K _____   **35** L _____   **36** M _____

> 12

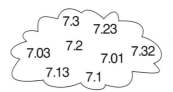

7.3   7.23   7.03   7.2   7.01   7.32   7.13   7.1

37–38 Which two numbers add to give 14.5?   _____   _____

39–40 Which two numbers subtract to give 0.27?   _____   _____

41–42 Which two numbers add to give 14.55?   _____   _____

43–44 Which two numbers subtract to give 0.31?   _____   _____

45–46 Which two numbers add to give 14.21?   _____   _____

> 10

47 Find the **lowest common multiple** of 3 and 4. _____

48 Find the lowest common multiple of 4 and 6. _____

49 Find the lowest common multiple of 2 and 5. _____

50 Find the lowest common multiple of 6 and 9. _____

| 4 |

| 50 |
| TOTAL |

Paper 18

IN   OUT

1–3

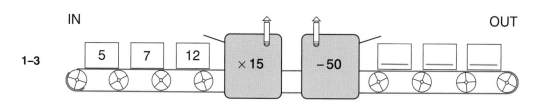

| 3 |

The letters from the word **BANANAS** are placed in a tub and a letter is taken out at random.

Writing your answers as fractions in their lowest terms, what is the probability of taking out letter:

4 S   _____   **5 A**   _____

6 N   _____   **7 T**   _____

| 4 |

Indicate which is the larger by writing > or < in each space.

8 24 × 4 _____ 25 + 60   **9** 9 + 8 − 4 _____ 20 − 2 − 6

10 5 × 11 _____ 7 × 8   **11** 9 × 12 _____ 10 × 11

12 7 × 10 _____ 6 × 12   **13** 3 + 7 + 9 _____ 2 + 9 + 6

| 6 |

For each of these shapes, give the area of the whole shape, the area of the shaded part and the area of the unshaded part.

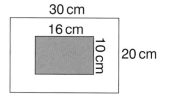

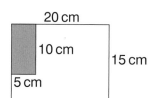

14 Area of whole _____   **17** Area of whole _____

15 Area of shaded part _____   **18** Area of shaded part _____

16 Area of unshaded part _____   **19** Area of unshaded part _____

| 6 |

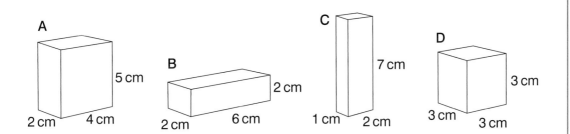

20 The volume of Figure A is _____

21 The volume of Figure B is _____

22 The capacity of Figure C is _____

23 The capacity of Figure D is _____

If the sides of each figure were twice as long,
the volume of each would be:

24 Figure A _____

25 Figure B _____

26 Figure C _____

27 Figure D _____

`8`

28–33 Complete the following table.

3	2	7	___	8	___	21	24
27	18	___	90	___	108	___	___

`6`

34 Felt-tip pens cost a shopkeeper £1.80 for 10.
    How many can he buy with £36.00? _____

35 Carelessly, Lena divided by 8 instead of multiplying
    by 8 and got an answer of 564. What should it have been? _____

`2`

What is the mode in each series of numbers below?

36 11 12 14 12 13 15   Mode is ____

37 7 9 8 6 9 5   Mode is ____

38 24 22 23 21 20 24   Mode is ____

39 6 3 3 5 3 4   Mode is ____

`4`

Foreign countries (outside Europe) are listed as Zone 1 or Zone 2 for postal charges (air mail).

Argentina, Brazil, Canada, Chile and Cuba are in Zone 1.

Tonga, New Zealand, the Philippines, Mongolia, Korea and Japan are in Zone 2.

Up to and including:	Zone 1	Zone 2
100 g	£2.05	£2.33
120 g	£2.40	£2.75
140 g	£2.75	£3.17
160 g	£3.10	£3.59
180 g	£3.45	£4.01
200 g	£3.80	£4.43

How much more does it cost to send:

40 a 140 g letter to New Zealand than to Canada? _____

41 a 170 g letter to Korea than to Chile? _____

42 a 110 g letter to Japan than to Cuba? _____

43 a 151 g letter to Mongolia than to Chile? _____

44 a 132 g letter to the Philippines than to Argentina? _____

5

45 What number when multiplied by 36 gives
the same answer as 42 × 18? _____

1

Describe the following polygons by name and say whether they are regular or irregular.

Example [square] regular quadrilateral

46 [rectangle] _____ quadrilateral

47–48 [octagon] _____ _____

49–50 [pentagon] _____ _____

5

50
TOTAL

Paper 19

1   The temperature increases by 6 °C from –2 °C.
    What is the new temperature?   _____°C

2   The temperature decreases by 13 °C from 4 °C.
    What is the new temperature?   _____°C   **2**

Complete the table below.

3–11

					mode	median	range
$10\frac{1}{2}$	23	2	$10\frac{1}{2}$		_____	_____	_____
56	221	34	221	–2	_____	_____	_____
33	–3	–65	–3	2	_____	_____	_____

9

12   Find the lowest common multiple (**LCM**) of 3 and 5.   _____

13   Find the LCM of 10 and 15.   _____

14   Find the LCM of 14 and 21.   _____

15   Find the LCM of 3 and 12.   _____   **4**

Prize money to the value of £50 is shared between two friends. Phil gets $\frac{3}{10}$ and
Kusum gets $\frac{7}{10}$.

16   Phil gets £ _____   17   Kusum gets £ _____   **2**

Here are the shoe sizes of 20 children. First complete the table below and then
complete the bar chart.

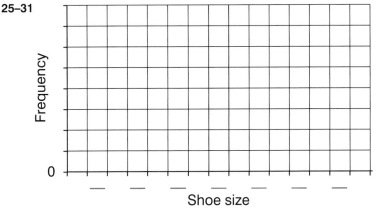

18–24

2	3	2	1	$1\frac{1}{2}$	$2\frac{1}{2}$	$1\frac{1}{2}$
$1\frac{1}{2}$	$2\frac{1}{2}$	$3\frac{1}{2}$	3	4	$2\frac{1}{2}$	4
3	$3\frac{1}{2}$	3	$2\frac{1}{2}$	4	$2\frac{1}{2}$	

Shoe size	Frequency
1	
$1\frac{1}{2}$	
2	
$2\frac{1}{2}$	
3	
$3\frac{1}{2}$	
4	

7

25–31

Frequency

0

Shoe size

7

32–34 Complete these shapes. The dashed line is the line of symmetry.

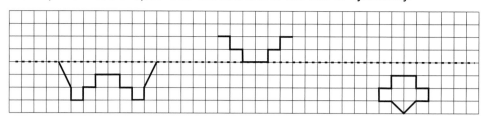

`3`

A bottle of concentrated orange drink holds 1.25 litres. Each glass holds 300 ml.
We need to put 50 ml of orange in each glass before adding water.

35 What fraction of the glass did the orange concentrate fill? _____

36 How many glasses could we make from a bottle of orange drink? _____

37 175 people asked for a drink. How many bottles of the
orange would be needed? _____

38 If each bottle costs 75p, how much would this be? _____

39 If we charged 10p a glass and sold all we had,
what profit would we make? _____

`5`

These scales are used to weigh 3 parcels. How much does each parcel cost to post?

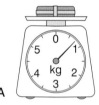

A

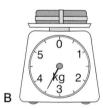

B

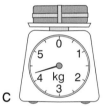

C

PARCELS Weight not over:	£
1 kg	5.60
2 kg	6.45
4 kg	8.25
6 kg	9.45
8 kg	10.50
10 kg	13.00

40 A would cost _____   **41** B would cost _____

42 C would cost _____   **43** How much less would it cost to send all 3
parcels as one large parcel? _____

`4`

Using a protractor, measure the following angles to the nearest 2°. They are all even numbers (e.g. 12° or 14°).

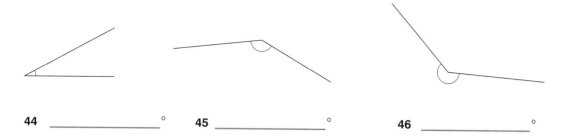

44 _____ °   45 _____ °   46 _____ °   **3**

Take two identical cubes and join them together by matching face to face so you cannot see the join.

For the new object find:

47 Number of faces   _____

48 Number of vertices _____

49 Number of edges   _____

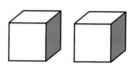

50 How many of the faces of the original cubes can you no longer see? _____   **4**

50
TOTAL

Paper 20

If the sum of the digits of a number are divisible by 9, then the number is divisible by 9.

Example 342   3 + 4 + 2 = 9   9 ÷ 9 = 1   so 342 is divisible by 9

1–3 Underline the numbers which are divisible by 9.

3114   57502   4123   75501   341583   3415833   **3**

Here are the petrol gauges of 4 cars.

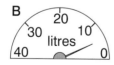  

A 16 24 8 litres 32 0

B 20 30 10 litres 40 0

C 18 27 9 litres 36 0

D 12 18 6 litres 24 0

Petrol costs 70p per litre. To fill up their tanks:

4–5 A would need _____ litres.   This would cost _____

6–7 B would need _____ litres.   This would cost _____

8–9 C would need _____ litres.   This would cost _____

10–11 D would need _____ litres.   This would cost _____   **8**

There are 12 balls in a bag; they are numbered 1 to 12. Writing your answers as fractions in their lowest terms:

12 What is the chance of picking an odd-numbered ball? _____

What is the chance of picking a ball which has:

13 a multiple of 3 on it? _____

14 a multiple of 5 on it? _____

15 a multiple of 7 on it? _____

4

Simplify the following expressions.

16 $15a - 4a + 5 - 3 =$ _____

17 $4b + 9b + 4 + 13 =$ _____

18 $3c + 4 + 5 - 6 - c =$ _____

19 $58p - 32p + 13 + 4 =$ _____

4

Underline the correct answer.

20 5^2 is   5   25   125

21 2.7 is between   2 and $2\frac{1}{4}$ $2\frac{1}{2}$ and 3 $2\frac{1}{4}$ and $2\frac{1}{2}$

22 $\sqrt{16}$ is   4   8   2

23 $1\frac{1}{1000}$ is   1.1   1.001   1.01

4

Underline the correct answer.

24 Degrees in half a right angle   50   60   90   45   120

25 Minutes in $2\frac{1}{2}$ hours   120   150   140   160   200

26 3^2 5   6   2   9   12

27 Hours in November   600   300   700   800   720

28 Millimetres in 2 metres   1000   100   2000   200   20

29 cm^3 in 1 litre   100   10   50   1000   2000

6

What fraction is shaded in the following circles? Write each fraction in its lowest terms.

30 _____   **31** _____   **32** _____   **33** _____

4

What is the total surface area of the following shapes?

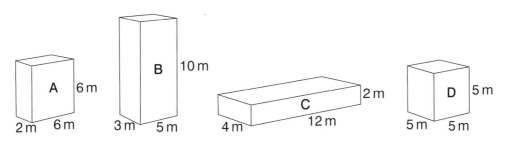

34 A _____   **35** B _____   **36** C _____   **37** D _____

What percentage of each shape is shaded? Write the answer in the space provided.

38 _____   **39** _____   **40** _____   **41** _____

42 _____   **43** _____   **44** _____   **45** _____

Write the next two terms in the following sequences.

46–47 1 4 9 16 25 _____ . _____

48–49 1 3 6 10 15 _____ _____

Sarah spends $\frac{1}{5}$ of the week at work sorting out paperwork. She works 45 hours per week.

50 How many hours of paperwork does Sarah do during two weeks?   _____

Paper 21

1

Angle p = _____ °

Convert the following measurements from metric to imperial or vice versa.

2 _____ kilograms ≈ 11 lb

3 2 kilometres ≈ _____ miles

4 _____ litres ≈ $10\frac{1}{2}$ pints

5 15 kilograms ≈ _____ lb

Metric	Imperial
1 litre	$1\frac{3}{4}$ pints
1 kilogram	2.2 lb
8 kilometres	5 miles

6 The temperature is –2 °C. It rises by 5 °C then falls by 8 °C.
What is the new temperature? _____ °C

7 The temperature is 3 °C. It falls by 9 °C, then rises by 4 °C.
What is the new temperature? _____ °C

Describe the following polygons by name and say whether they are regular or irregular.

8–9

_____ _____

10–11

_____ _____

12–13

_____ _____

Work out the following.

14 $\frac{3}{7}$ of €42 = € _____

15 $\frac{4}{7}$ of €4200 = € _____

Translate the following shape A. Draw and label its new location.

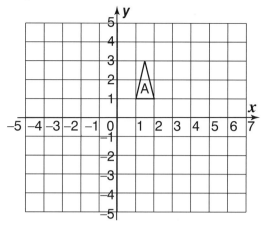

$\mathbf{b} = \begin{pmatrix} 2 \\ 0 \end{pmatrix}$ $\mathbf{c} = \begin{pmatrix} -3 \\ 0 \end{pmatrix}$ $\mathbf{d} = \begin{pmatrix} 0 \\ 2 \end{pmatrix}$ $\mathbf{e} = \begin{pmatrix} -4 \\ 0 \end{pmatrix}$ $\mathbf{f} = \begin{pmatrix} 4 \\ -4 \end{pmatrix}$

16 Translate A by **b** to B.   **17** Translate A by **c** to C.

18 Translate A by **d** to D.   **19** Translate A by **e** to E.

20 Translate A by **f** to F.

What is the volume of these cuboids? They are made from 1 cm cubes.

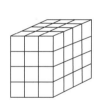 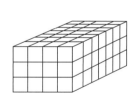 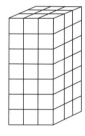 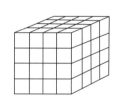

21 _____ cm³   **22** _____ cm³   **23** _____ cm³   **24** _____ cm³

If another layer of 1 cm cubes was placed on top of each cuboid what would the volume be now?

25 _____ cm³   **26** _____ cm³   **27** _____ cm³   **28** _____ cm³

29 Find the difference between six thousand and six and 4567.   _____

30–34 Place these **integers** in order from **smallest** to **largest**.

    −4   21   −3   0   2

35 Circle the LCM of 8 and 10.

    8   10   24   40   80   800

5

4

4

1

5

36 Circle the LCM of 24 and 18.

18   24   48   72   180   240

37 Circle the LCM of 15 and 20.

15   20   35   40   60   300

The ages of our family add up to 85 years. I am 10 years old, Dad is $3\frac{1}{2}$ times as old as I am. My sister is 2 years younger than I am and Mum is 4 times as old as my sister.

38 Mum is _____   **39** Dad is _____   **40** My sister is _____

Remember to work out brackets first, then × and ÷ then + and –.

Find the answers to the following:

41 $(4 + 5) - 5 \div 2$ _____   **42** $22 + 18 \times (9 + 1)$ _____

43 $(19 + 25) \div 4 - 2$ _____   **44** $64 + 26 \div 2$ _____

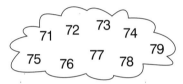

45–46 Write the multiples of 4 from the numbers in the bubble.   _____ _____

47–49 Write the multiples of 3 from the numbers in the bubble.   _____ _____ _____

50 Write the multiple of 9 from the numbers in the bubble.   _____

Paper 22

What is the order of rotational symmetry of each of the following shapes?

1   _____

2   Equilateral triangle   _____

3   _____

Give the answers to the following in their lowest terms:

4 $\frac{7}{8} \times \frac{40}{49}$ = _____

5 $\frac{4}{9} \times \frac{27}{24}$ = _____

6 $\frac{5}{11} \times \frac{66}{50}$ = _____

7 $\frac{4}{5} \times \frac{20}{28}$ = _____

Find the areas of the following right-angled triangles.

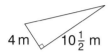
$2\frac{1}{2}$ cm

8 cm

8 Area = _____ cm²

4.6 cm

2 cm

9 Area = _____ cm²

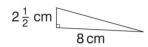
4 m $10\frac{1}{2}$ m

10 Area = _____ m²

6 m   3 m

11 Area = _____ m²

12 Three numbers multiplied together give 2618. One number is 11 and another is 14. What is the third number? _____

The answers to the following questions will be found in this sausage shape.

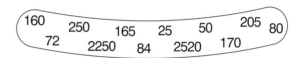
160   250   165   25   50   205   80
72   2250   84   2520   170

13 How many minutes in $2\frac{3}{4}$ hours? _____ mins

14 How many cm in 2.5 metres? _____ cm

15 How many mm in 2.25 metres? _____ mm

16–31 Insert a sign in each space to make each line and column work out to the given answer.

2		3		4	=	10
4		1		2	=	3
2		4		3	=	5
=		=		=		=
8		−1		5	=	2

32–36 What are the prime numbers more than 25 and less than 45?

_____   _____   _____   _____   _____

37–41 Draw lines to join up the statements which are equal.

Multiply by four then add three then add two $2n - 3$

Multiply by three then add nine then take two $4n + 5$

Divide by two then multiply by four then subtract three $3(n + 2) - 4$

Divide by three then subtract two then add five $\frac{n}{3} + 3$

Add two then multiply by three then take four $3n + 7$

Answer the following questions only using these words.

Certain   Likely   Unlikely   Impossible

42 A dinosaur will walk down your street tomorrow.   _____

43 I will find some money on the pavement tomorrow.   _____

44 I will roll a six on a single throw with a fair 6-sided dice.   _____

45 I will roll a number higher than two with a fair 6-sided dice.   _____

Here are some nets. Some will make a cuboid and some will not. Write either 'true' if they will or 'false' if they will not.

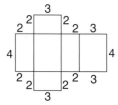   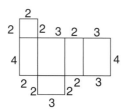   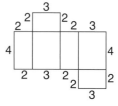

46 _____   **47** _____   **48** _____

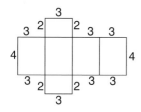   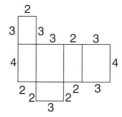

49 _____   **50** _____

5

5

4

5

50
TOTAL

Paper 23

1 The temperature is –6 °C. It rises by 15 °C then falls by 20 °C.
What is the new temperature?   _____ °C

2 The temperature is 13 °C. It falls by 19 °C then rises by 6 °C.
What is the new temperature?   _____ °C

3 The temperature is –13 °C. It falls by 17 °C then rises by 2 °C.
What is the new temperature?   _____ °C   3

Find the surface area of these cuboids.

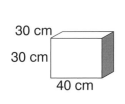

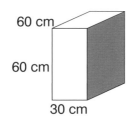

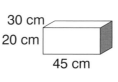

4 _____ cm²   5 _____ cm²   6 _____ cm²   3

Translate the following shape A. Draw and label its new location.

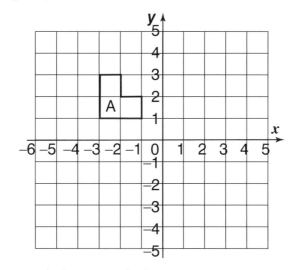

$\mathbf{b} = \begin{pmatrix} 5 \\ 2 \end{pmatrix}$ $\mathbf{c} = \begin{pmatrix} 4 \\ -2 \end{pmatrix}$ $\mathbf{d} = \begin{pmatrix} -1 \\ -4 \end{pmatrix}$ $\mathbf{e} = \begin{pmatrix} -2 \\ 2 \end{pmatrix}$ $\mathbf{f} = \begin{pmatrix} 2 \\ -5 \end{pmatrix}$

7 Translate A by **b** to B.   8 Translate A by **c** to C.

9 Translate A by **d** to D.   10 Translate A by **e** to E.

11 Translate A by **f** to F.   5

Write the number which has a:

12 7 in the tenths place _____

13 5 in the tens place _____

14 2 in the units place _____

15 6 in the thousandths place _____

16 1 in the hundreds place _____

17 8 in the hundredths place _____

125.678
812.567
789.256
678.125
567.812
256.781

6

Convert the following measurements from metric to imperial or vice versa.

Metric	Imperial
1 litre	$1\frac{3}{4}$ pints
1 kilogram	2.2 lb
8 kilometres	5 miles

18 42 litres ≈ _____ pints

19 1000 kilograms ≈ _____ lb

20 72 kilometres ≈ _____ miles

21 _____ kilometres ≈ $27\frac{1}{2}$ miles

22 _____ litres ≈ 16 pints

5

23 What number multiplied by 45 will give the same answer as 65 × 27? _____

1

Indicate which is larger by writing > or < in each space.

24 £0.46 _____ 56p

25 €4.50 _____ €5

26 0.245 kg _____ 0.254 kg

27 3.14 _____ 3.142

4

Complete the table below.

28–36

							mode	median	range
100	300	99	10000		45		____	____	____
−4	−7	−11	−7				____	____	____
$\frac{1}{2}$	$\frac{3}{4}$	$\frac{1}{2}$	$\frac{3}{4}$	$\frac{1}{2}$	$\frac{3}{4}$	$\frac{1}{2}$	____	____	____

9

Here are the ages of six friends.

	years	months
Simon	11	6
Emilie	10	11
Pippa	11	1
Milo	10	10
Ravi	11	11
Matthew	11	3

37 Their ages add up to: _____

38 Their average age is: _____

39 Another girl joins them and their average age is now
11 years 2 months. How old is the newcomer? _____

40–41 Find the common factors of 15 and 18. _____ _____

42–45 Find the common factors of 24 and 32. _____ _____ _____ _____

46–50 Complete the table of values to satisfy the rule $y = 2x + 8$.

x	−2	−1	0	1	2	3
$y = 2x + 8$	___	___	___	___	12	___

Paper 24

Find the areas of the following right-angled triangles.

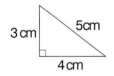
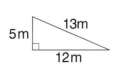
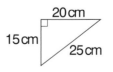

1 _____ cm²   **2** _____ m²   **3** _____ cm²   **4** _____ m²

5 805	**6** 904	**7** 590	**8** 860
× 407	× 760	× 609	× 570

9–12 Draw four **different** nets of a closed cube (six square faces) on the grid below. None of your answers should be reflections or rotations of one another.

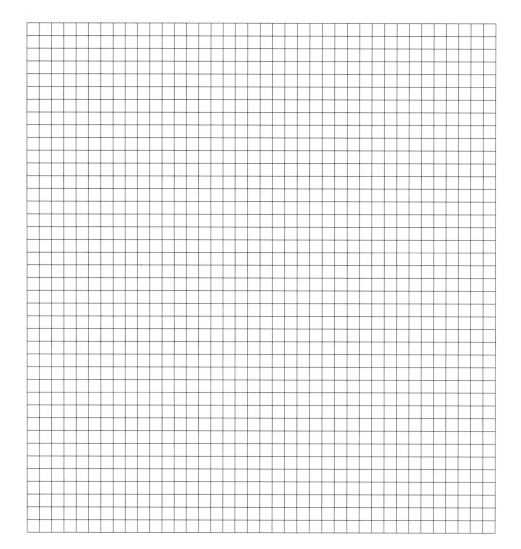

Three sums of money total £100. The largest amount is £46.80, the second largest is three times as large as the smallest.

13 The second largest amount is _____

14 The smallest amount is _____

Answer the following. Use mixed numbers where appropriate and write fractions in their lowest terms.

15 $1\frac{1}{2} \div 1\frac{3}{4} =$ _____

16 $1\frac{3}{4} \div 3\frac{1}{2} =$ _____

17 $2\frac{1}{4} \div 1\frac{1}{2} =$ _____

18 $3\frac{2}{3} \div 1\frac{5}{6} =$ _____

4

19 Find the **highest common factor** (**HCF**) of 40 and 65. _____

20 Find the HCF of 14 and 35. _____

21 Find the HCF of 30 and 48. _____

22 Find the HCF of 10 and 120. _____

23 Find the HCF of 26 and 30. _____

24 Find the HCF of 20 and 44. _____

25 Find the HCF of 36 and 63. _____

7

264 children go home from school by train. One-third of them get off at the first station and $\frac{5}{8}$ of these children are girls.

26 How many girls leave the train at the first station? _____

27 How many boys leave the train at the first station? _____

28 How many children get off after the first station? _____

3

In a village the population is 1010. The men and women together number 451 and the women and children together number 795.

29–31 There are _____ men _____ women _____ children

3

32 I have £9.00. How many magazines, each costing 59p, can I buy? _____

1

33–35 If the last two digits of a number are divisible by 4 then the number is divisible by 4.

Example   3424   24 ÷ 4 = 6   so 3424 is divisible by 4.

Underline the numbers which are divisible by 4.

3114   57532   4123   75503   341588   3415820

3

Write < or > in each space below.

36 11^2 _____ 110

37 35 mins _____ $\frac{2}{3}$ hour

2

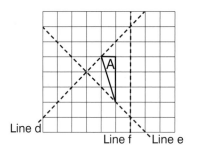

38 Reflect shape A in mirror line d. Label it D.

39 Reflect shape A in mirror line e. Label it E.

40 Reflect shape A in mirror line f. Label it F.

> 3

All these rectangles have the same perimeter. Find the missing lengths and the areas.

41–48

Length	Width	Area
10 cm	8 cm	80 cm²
_____	3 cm	_____
1 cm	_____	_____
_____	2.5 cm	_____
_____	_____	81 cm²

> 8

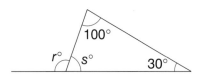

49 Angle r = _____ °

50 Angle s = _____ °

> 2

> 50
> TOTAL